GRADE 2

Treasure Chest

For English Language Learners

Retelling Cards

Blackline Masters

Macmillan McGraw-Hill

Contents

Retelling Cards

Blackline Masters

Preparing the Retelling Cards

Retelling Cards Blackline Masters are black and white copies of the images from the Retelling Cards in *Treasure Chest*. They provide visual prompts for English Language Learners to retell the stories they have read in class.

- Make copies of Retelling Cards Blackline Masters for each student.
- Have students cut the cards along the dotted lines.

Using the Retelling Cards

- **Practice Retelling**

  Retelling Cards Blackline Masters help students develop comprehension. Students can use the Blackline Masters independently to work in pairs or groups:

  - Sort the cards and retell the story in their own words
  - Incorporate the weekly vocabulary words
  - Make personal connections to the book

- **Home-School Connection**

  Encourage students to take the Blackline Masters home to share what they have learned in class with their families. This will help improve their oral development and literacy skills. Students can retell in their native language.

School Star

School Star

School Star

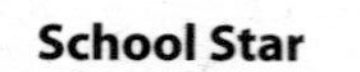

School Star

School Star

School Star

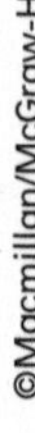

City Garden

City Garden

Please sign our letter to the mayor. We want to make a garden.

City Garden

City Garden

Call 911!

Call 911!

Call 911!

Call 911!

Call 911!

Call 911!

Guide Dogs

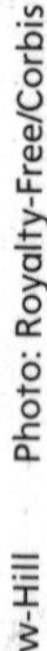

Guide Dogs

Guide Dogs

Guide Dogs

Guide Dogs

Guide Dogs

Remember Me

Remember Me

©Macmillan/McGraw-Hill

Remember Me

Remember Me

Plants You Can Eat

 Photo: (t) PhotoLink/Getty Images; (b) Corel

Plants You Can Eat

 Photo: (tl, tr) C Squared Studios/Getty Images; (bl) Royalty-Free/Corbis; (br) Brand X Pictures/Getty Images

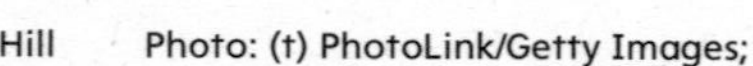

Plants You Can Eat

 Photo: (tl) Corel; (tc) Brian Hagiwara/Getty Images; (tr) Photodisc; (b) Mary-Kate Denny/Alamy

Plants You Can Eat

 Photo: Renee Comet/Getty Image

Plants You Can Eat

 Photo: Howard Sokol/Picture Quest

Plants You Can Eat

 Photo: (l) C Squared Studios/Getty Images; (r) Royalty-Free/Corbis

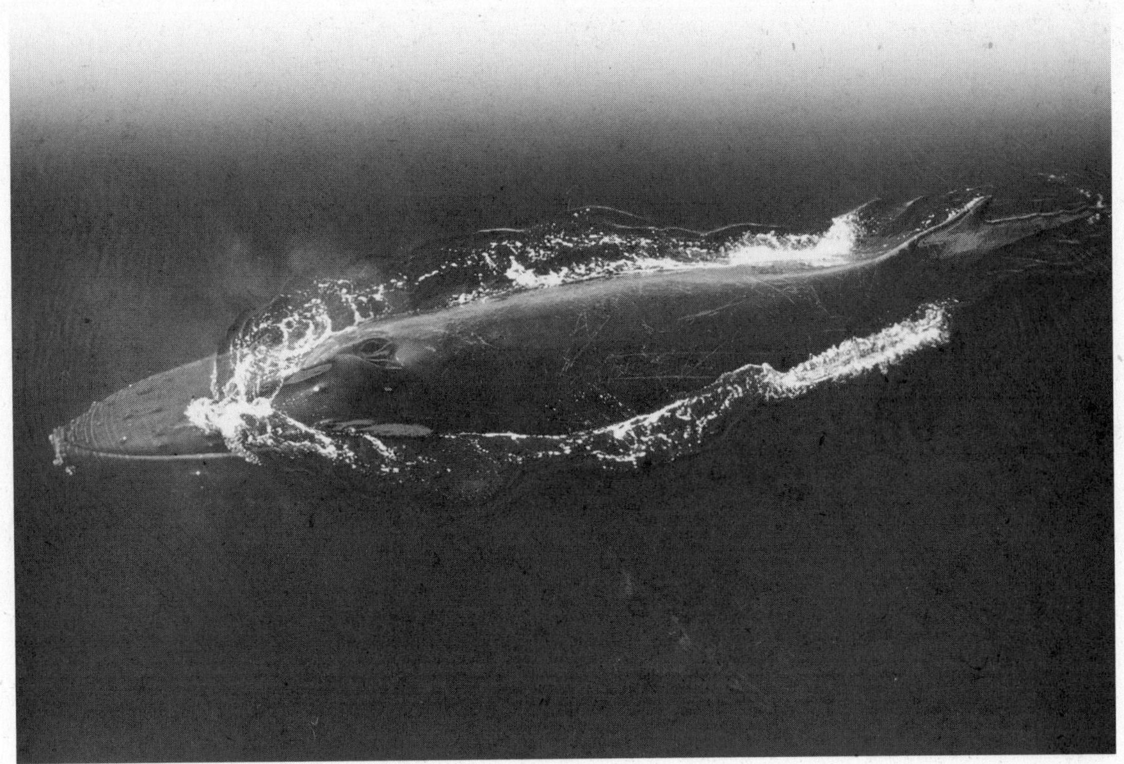

Whale Watch

Whale Watch

Whale Watch

Whale Watch

 Photo: Photofusion Picture Library/Alamy

Whale Watch

 Photo: Gabriel RojoNature Picture Library

Whale Watch

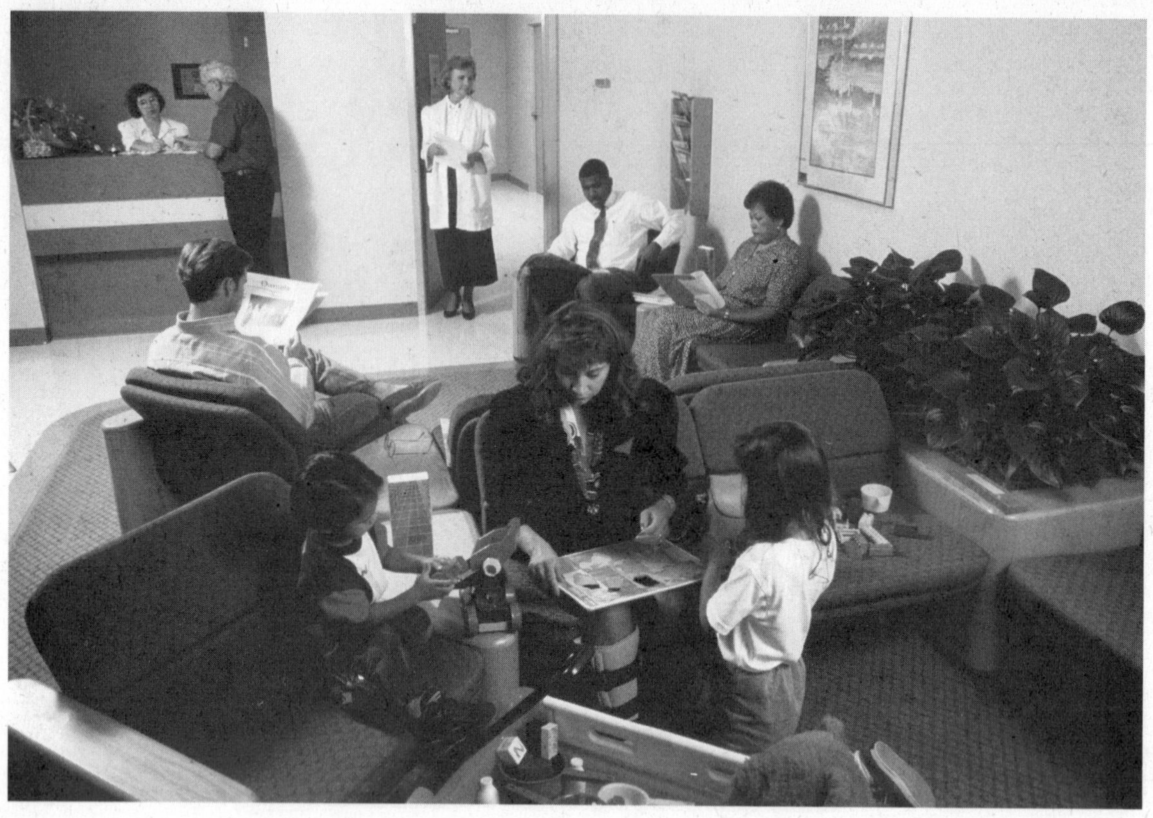

©Macmillan/McGraw-Hill Photo: Chronis Jons/Getty Images

Hospital Helpers

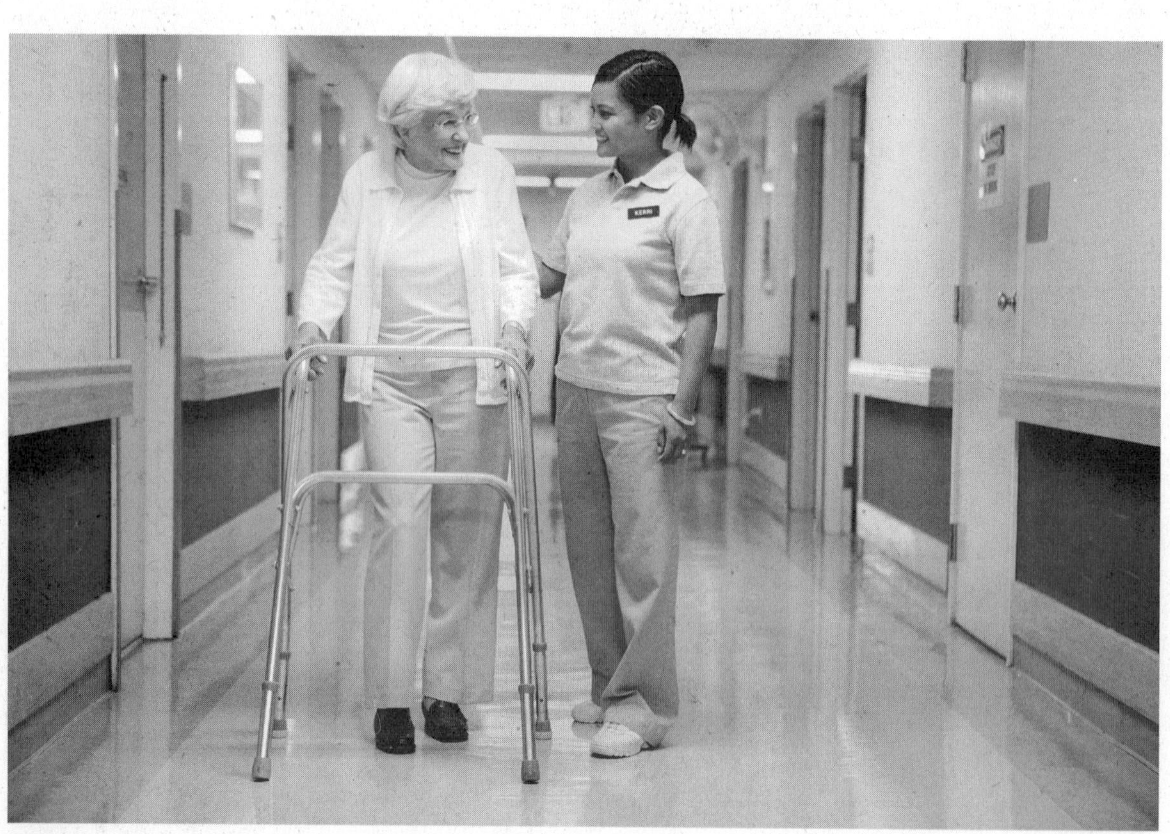

©Macmillan/McGraw-Hill Photo: Andersen Ross/Getty Images

Hospital Helpers

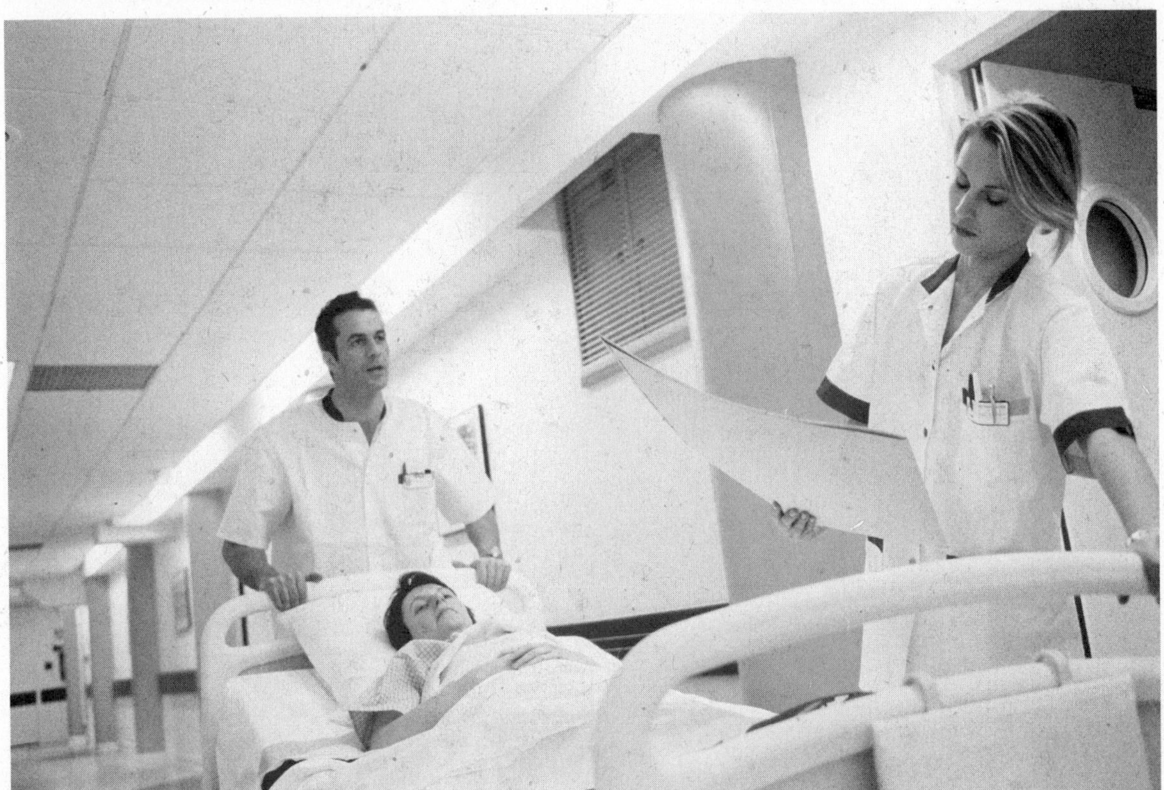

Hospital Helpers

Hospital Helpers

Hospital Helpers

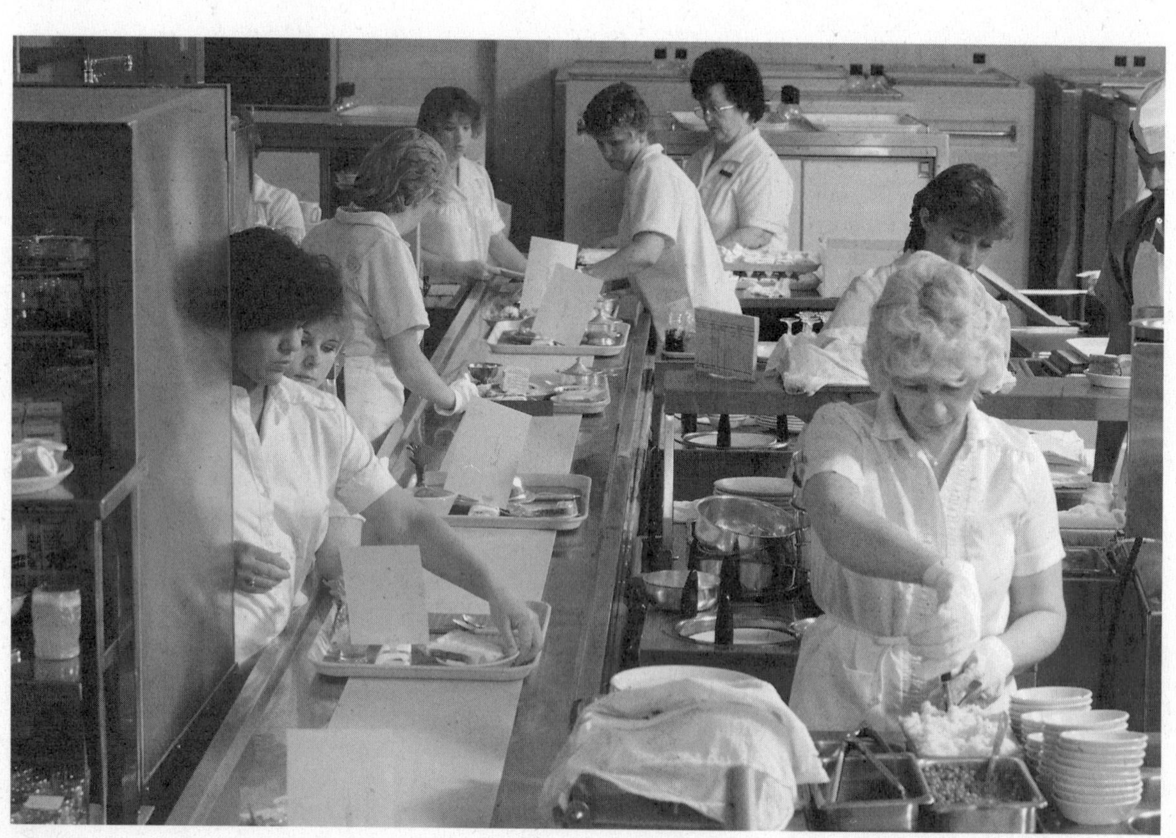

Hospital Helpers

Little Bat

Little Bat

Little Bat

Little Bat

Little Bat

Little Bat

Tom's Tryouts

Tom's Tryouts

Tom's Tryouts

Tom's Tryouts

Tom's Tryouts

Tom's Tryouts

Wasted Wishes

Wasted Wishes

Wasted Wishes

Wasted Wishes

Wasted Wishes

Wasted Wishes

Photo: BananaStock/Age Fotostock

Home Safety

Photo: Martin Chaffer/Getty Images

Home Safety

Home Safety

Home Safety

Photo: Corbis Royalty-Free

Home Safety

Photo: Mary Kate Denny/Photo Edit

Home Safety

100-Year-Old Animals

100-Year-Old Animals

100-Year-Old Animals

100-Year-Old Animals

Photo: Amos Nachoum/Corbis

100-Year-Old Animals

Photo: (tl) Jochen Tack/Peter Arnold, Inc.; (tr) Cousteau Society/Getty Images; (tc) Jeff Rotman/Alamy

100-Year-Old Animals

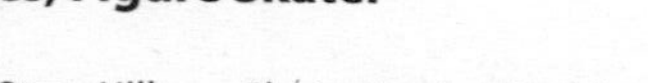

Sarah Hughes, Figure Skater

 Photo: Reuters/Corbis

Sarah Hughes, Figure Skater

 Photo: Neal Preston/Corbis

Sarah Hughes, Figure Skater

 Photo: Cliff Schiappa/AP Photo

Sarah Hughes, Figure Skater

 Photo: John Macdougall/AFP/Getty Images

Sarah Hughes, Figure Skater

 Photo: Ed Betz/AP Photo

Sarah Hughes, Figure Skater

 Photo: Jacques Demarthon/AFP/Getty Images

Where Are the Eggs?

Where Are the Eggs?

Where Are the Eggs?

Where Are the Eggs?

Where Are the Eggs?

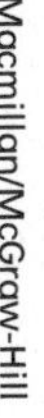

Where Are the Eggs?

Yaks of the Mountains

Yaks of the Mountains

Yaks of the Mountains

Yaks of the Mountains

Yaks of the Mountains

Yaks of the Mountains

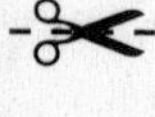

Dolphin Rescue

Dolphin Rescue

Dolphin Rescue

Dolphin Rescue

Dolphin Rescue

Dolphin Rescue

 Photo: SuperStock, Inc/SuperStock

What Happens to Your Trash?

 Photo: Stephen Ferry/Liaison/Getty Images

What Happens to Your Trash?

What Happens to Your Trash?

What Happens to Your Trash?

What Happens to Your Trash?

What Happens to Your Trash?

The Sled

The Sled

The Sled

The Sled

The Sled

The Sled

The Rainforest

The Rainforest

The Rainforest

The Rainforest

The Rainforest

The Rainforest

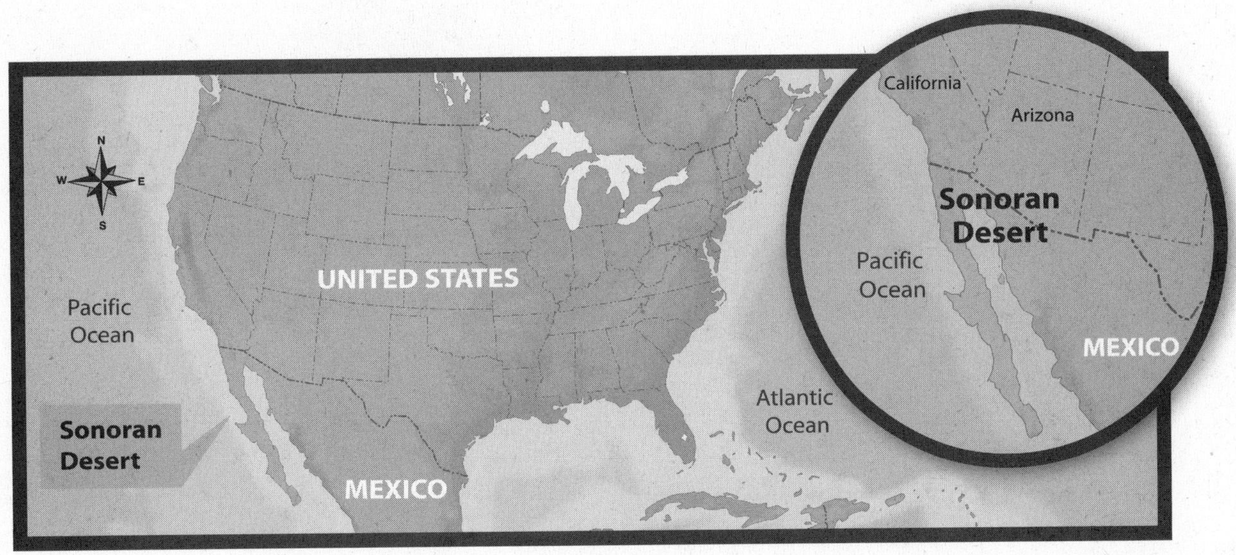

Sonoran Desert Animals

Sonoran Desert Animals

Sonoran Desert Animals

Sonoran Desert Animals

Sonoran Desert Animals

Sonoran Desert Animals

Sky Colors

Sky Colors

Sky Colors

Sky Colors

Sky Colors

Sky Colors

Discovering Shipwrecks

Discovering Shipwrecks

Discovering Shipwrecks

Discovering Shipwrecks

Discovering Shipwrecks

Discovering Shipwrecks

Photo: A.J.J. Estudi/Age Fotostock

All About Pumpkins

Photo: (tl) Dwight Kuhn; (bl) Dwight Kuhn; (tr) Alan & Linda Detrick/Photo Researchers, Inc.; (br) Royalty-Free/Corbis

All About Pumpkins

All About Pumpkins

All About Pumpkins

All About Pumpkins

All About Pumpkins

Let's Visit Space

Let's Visit Space

Photo: Masterfile (Royalty Free Div.)

Let's Visit Space

Photo: Detlev Van Ravenswaay/Science Photo Library

Let's Visit Space

Let's Visit Space

Let's Visit Space

Saving Sofia

Saving Sofia

Saving Sofia

Saving Sofia

Saving Sofia

Saving Sofia

©Macmillan/McGraw-Hill Photo: Mary Altaffer/AP Photo

Illustrators at Work

©Macmillan/McGraw-Hill Photo: Photo: Ryan McVay/Getty Images

Illustrators at Work

Illustrators at Work

Illustrators at Work

Illustrators at Work

Illustrators at Work

A World of Colors

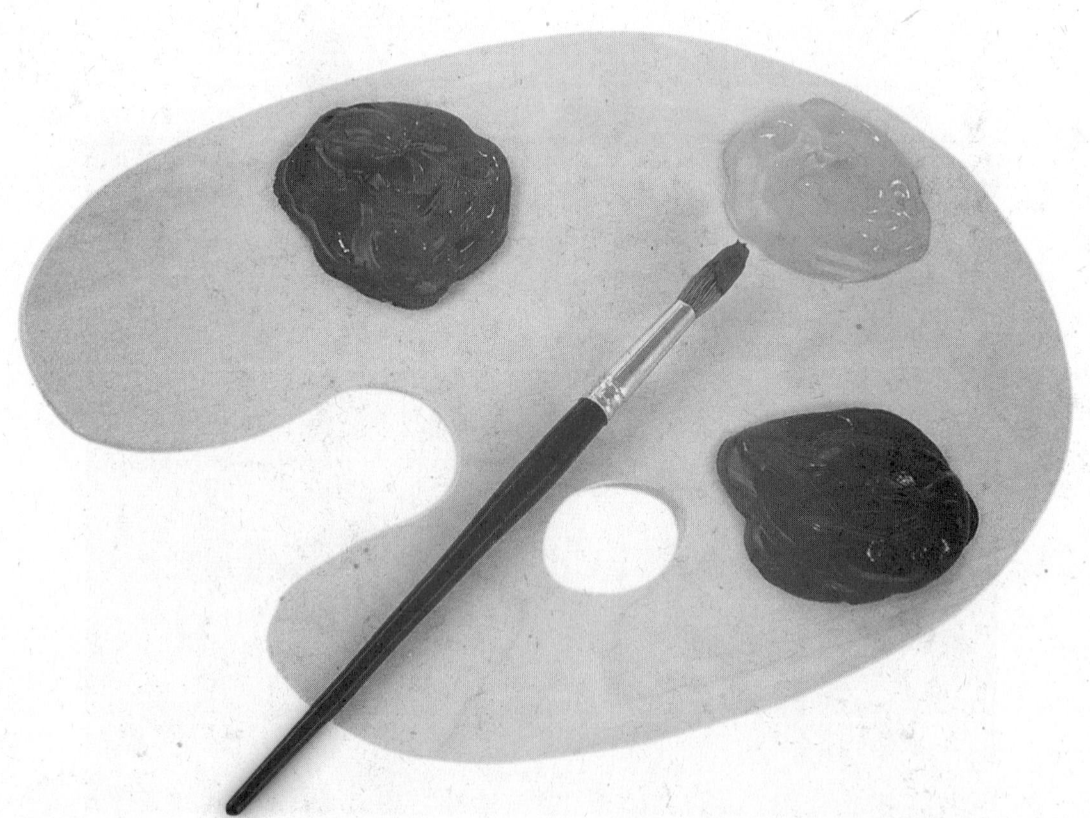

A World of Colors

 Photo: Francis G. Mayer/Corbis

A World of Colors

 Photo: Mark Tomalty/Masterfile

A World of Colors

 Photo: (tl) Steve Kaufman/Corbis; (tr) Gary W. Carter/Corbis

A World of Colors

 Photo: Archivo Iconografico, S.A./Corbis

A World of Colors

Telephones Then and Now

 Photo: Corbis

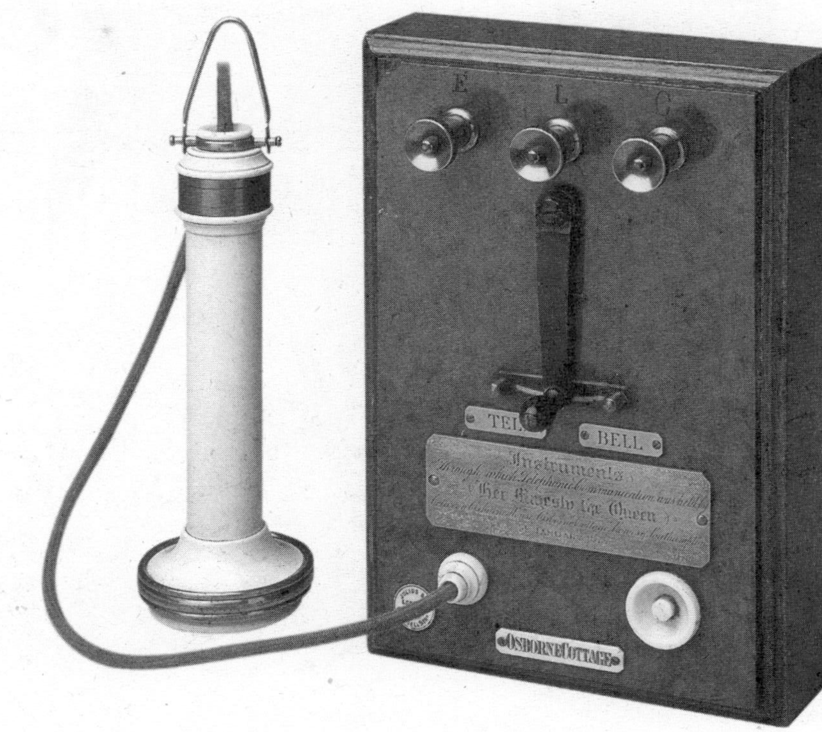

Telephones Then and Now

 Photo: SSPL/The Image Works

Telephones Then and Now

 Photo: Image Source/Getty Images

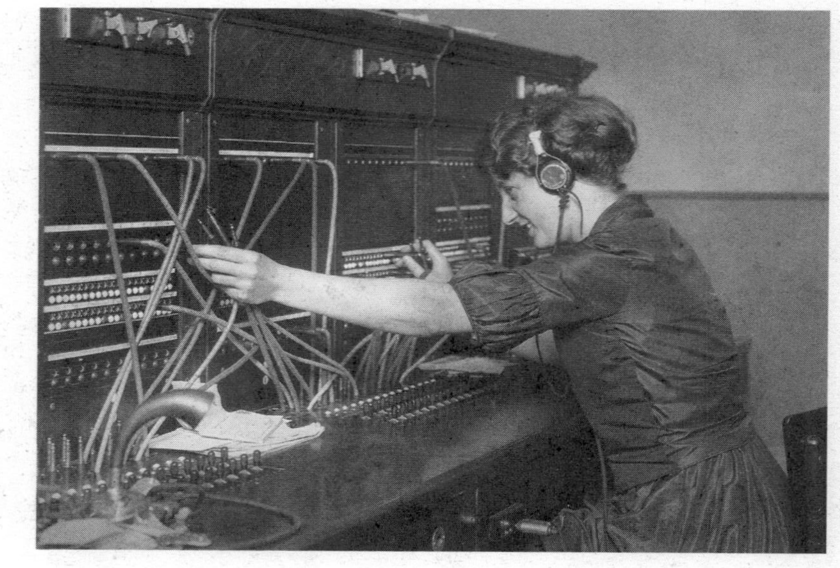

Telephones Then and Now

 Photo: Minnesota Historical Society/Corbis

Telephones Then and Now

 Photo: Victoria Arocho/AP Photo

Telephones Then and Now

 Photo: bl) Ryan McVay/Getty Images; (br) Thinkstock/Indexstock

Ice Cool

Ice Cool

Ice Cool

Ice Cool

Ice Cool

Ice Cool